So Much To See

Howie Groff

Illustrated by Olya Bond

ISBN #979-8-88862-863-8 Paperback
ISBN: #979-8-88862-864-5   Hardcover

For everyone who is hopeful for an exciting future.
May your enthusiasm be sweetly seasoned with patience.

-Howie Groff

Oh, lucky day—
the wind was just right.
Ky and his sister
love flying their Kite.

It is their special time
to imagine new things.
Kate said "Higher!"
as Ky held the string.

"Let's rhyme to life—
A new leaf of spring."
"We'll name her Lea."
"Let's hear her sing."

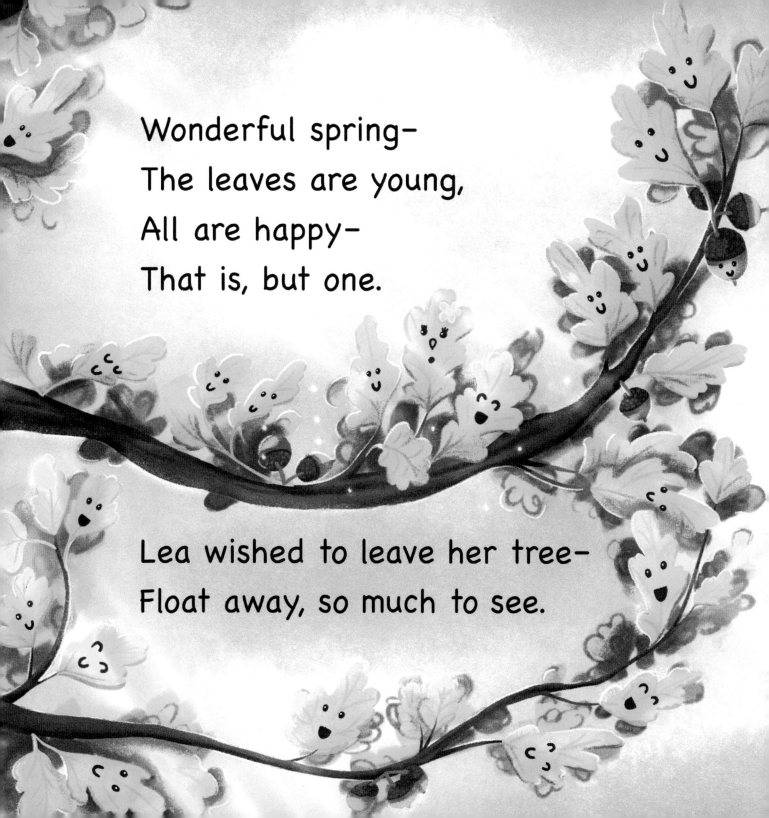

Wonderful spring–
The leaves are young,
All are happy–
That is, but one.

Lea wished to leave her tree–
Float away, so much to see.

The snow had gone,
And the sky was clear.
The trees breathed deep—
New life was here.

The robins were singing
And wisping around.
The squirrels were dashing
All over the ground.

All the leaves
Were growing strong,
Enjoying their home—
Enjoying the song.

But Lea wished to leave her tree—
Float away, so much to see.

"It's only spring,"
Big Oak said.
"You must wait
Till you turn red.

You are green,
And that's just fine.
Enjoy your home
Until your time."

When summer came
The air turned hot.
Lea was growing—
Her patience was not.

"Oh, blow, wind blow!
Please sweep me away.
I've been here too long,
And cannot stay."

"Whoa! Slow down Lea,"
Big Oak said.
"You are still green,
You must turn red."

But Lea still wished to leave her tree—
Float away, so much to see.

"Look at the flowers
And the bees in the air.
See them blossom.
Oh, the beauty they share.

It's a grand design—
We all have a part.
But joy in the moment
Must come from the heart."

The autumn winds came,
Bringing a change.
Lea turned orange–
She felt quite strange.

While the other leaves
Were floating away,
It was not clear
Why Lea must stay.

Then a strong gust blew
And tossed her about.
It tickled her inside—
Then a giggle came out.

All the leaves were gone—
That it, but one.
It took all year,
But Lea had fun.

NOW Lea was ready to leave her tree—

She floated away, So Much to See!

Romans 8:25

Now if we hope for what we do not see, we eagerly wait for it with patience.

- Christian Standard Bible